The children were all painting.
The Head Teacher opened the door.
'Can I talk to you about the
school trip, Mr Belter?' she said.
'It will not take long.'

'Do not stop painting,' said Mr Belter.
'Go on with what you are doing.'

Mr Belter and the Head Teacher
talked outside the door.
'Mr Belter can not see me now,' said Tessa.
'I will do a quick painting.'

'I will do a quick painting on the window,'
said Tessa.
'Do not let the paint fall out of the tin,'
said Tony.
But Tessa let some of the red paint
fall on her hand.

4

Tessa began to paint on the window.
'I will paint Mr Belter,' said Tessa.

'Quick,' said Tony.
'Here is Mr Belter.'
Tessa jumped down.

Tessa put her red paint tin
on the table by Kevin.
'Take that paint tin away,' said Kevin.
Mr Belter came in.

Mr Belter began to talk about a school trip.
'We will all go up to the top of a hill,'
he said, 'and we will...'
Mr Belter saw the window.
'Who did that?' he shouted.
He looked at the red paint tin by Kevin.
'Did you do that, Kevin?' he said.
'No,' said Kevin. 'It was not me.'

8

Mr Belter looked at the paint tins by Rocky.
'Did you do that, Rocky?' said Mr Belter.
'No,' said Rocky. 'It was not me.'

Mr Belter went over to Tony and Tessa.
Tessa saw that her hands were red.
'Did you do that, Tony?' said Mr Belter.
'No,' said Tony. 'It was not me.'

Mr Belter looked at the paint tins by Tessa.
'Did you do that, Tessa?' said Mr Belter.
'No,' said Tessa. 'It was not me.'

Mr Belter looked around the room.
Who had painted on the window?

Mr Belter went over to Kevin and
picked up his painting.
'Look at this good painting by Kevin,'
said Mr Belter.
'Can you see what it is?'
'It is a pile of mustard powder,' said Tony.

'It is not,' said Kevin.
'It is a canary.
You can see the wings.'
'Yes,' said Mr Belter.
'It is a good painting of a canary,
but do you know what Kevin
missed out of the rainbow?' he asked.
'Quick, hands up!'

14

Later, Mr Belter said,
'You can all go out now,
but I want to see Tessa about
the painting on the window.'

STOP!
How did Mr Belter know that it was Tessa
who painted on the window?
Do you know?
(See p 16.)

Mr Belter saw red paint on the window.
He saw that some of the paint came off a hand.
Mr Belter saw that Kevin had not
put red in his rainbow.
Mr Belter asked about the rainbow, and
he saw that only Tessa had
red paint on her hand!

16